The VW Book

by Lynn Maslen Kertell
pictures by Sue Hendra and John R. Maslen

Scholastic Inc.
New York • Toronto • London • Auckland • Sydney • Mexico City • New Delhi • Hong Kong • Buenos Aires

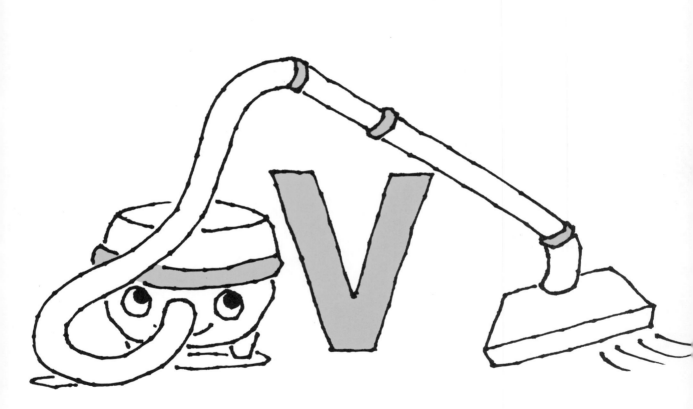

Vacuum

vultures

Vultures on vacation eat

vanilla ice cream.

Watermelons

wagon

Weasel, walrus, and woodpecker

devour wolf's wonderful watermelons.

Vacationing vultures would

welcome watermelon.

Look for these **v** and **w** words in this book.

vacation	wagon
vacationing	walrus
vacuum	watermelon(s)
vanilla	weasel
vultures	welcome
	wolf's
	wonderful
	woodpecker
	would

Look for these additional **v and w** words in the pictures: valentine, volcano, watch, wheels, and worm.